Help with Homework

First French

Here's a short note to parents:
These fun activities are designed to supplement French language teaching taught in school and to build up a vocabulary of useful French words and phrases. There are pronunciation guides, too, to help with unfamiliar words. It is recommended that you spend time with your child while doing any kind of school practice, to offer encouragement and guidance. Most of all, we hope you enjoy sharing this book together!

Written by Nina Filipek
Designed and illustrated by Jeannette O'Toole
Cover design by Dan Green

Autumn
Publishing

www.autumnchildrensbooks.co.uk

How do you say...?

Learn how to say the sounds of the letters. If you don't know how to say a word you can follow the pronunciation guide set within the brackets.

Vowels

a (as in b**a**t) for **salon** (salohn)

à (as in **a**nt) for **là** (la)

â (as in p**a**sta) for **pâtes** (paht)

é (as in caf**e**) for **marché** (marshay)

è (as in **e**gg) for **père** (pear)

i (as in f**i**eld) for **il** (eel)

î (as in f**i**eld) for **île** (eeluh)

o (as in g**o**t) for **bonne** (bon)

ô (as in **o**val) for **hôtel** (ohtel)

oe (as 'ir' in b**ir**d) **sœur** (sir)

u (as in r**u**de) for **rue** (roo)

ù (as in t**u**be) for **où** (ooh)

Nasal sounds

These nasal sounds are pronounced 'through the nose'. Look out for them when a vowel appears before an 'n'.

ans (ahn)

médecin (maydesan)

bon (bohn)

un (un)

chien (sheyan)

Consonants

French consonants are pronounced more clearly than English consonants, e.g. the 'r' is 'rolled' at the back of the mouth. However, there are some exceptions: 'h' is never pronounced.

homme (om)

hôtel (ohtel)

Place your star sticker here

Male and female nouns

In French, nouns (i.e. people, places and things) are either masculine (**un** or **le**) or feminine (**une** or **la**).

For example:

Masculine

un chien – a dog
le chien – the dog

Place your sticker here

Feminine

une maison – a house
la maison – the house

A French dictionary will tell you whether a noun is masculine or feminine.

Syllables

In English, we tend to stress the first part of a word and then 'slur' the remaining syllables. In French, the last syllable is stressed. Try it:

professeur (pro-fess-ur)

conversation (con-ver-sas-iyon)

Plurals

Add 's' to the noun unless it ends in s, x or z in which case there is no change. Add 'x' when the noun ends in eau and eu.

For example:

un fils – a son
les fils – the sons

un gâteau – a cake
les gâteaux – the cakes

Place your star sticker here

Let's talk

Learn these useful French phrases:

Salut! – Hello!

Pardon – I'm sorry

Bonjour – Good day

Bonsoir – Good evening

Au revoir – Goodbye

Ça va? – How are you?

Ça va bien, merci – Fine, thank you

Merci beaucoup – Thank you very much

Je vous en prie – Don't mention it

Comment vous appelez-vous? – What's your name?

Je m'appelle Jack – My name is Jack

S'il vous plaît – Please

Je ne comprends pas – I don't understand

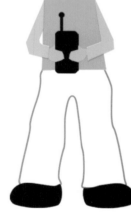

Say in French:

Thank you very much.

What's your name?

I don't understand.

How are you?

Place your star sticker here

Learn to ask these questions in French.
Find the stickers and put them in place.
Follow the phone lines to find a French speaker.

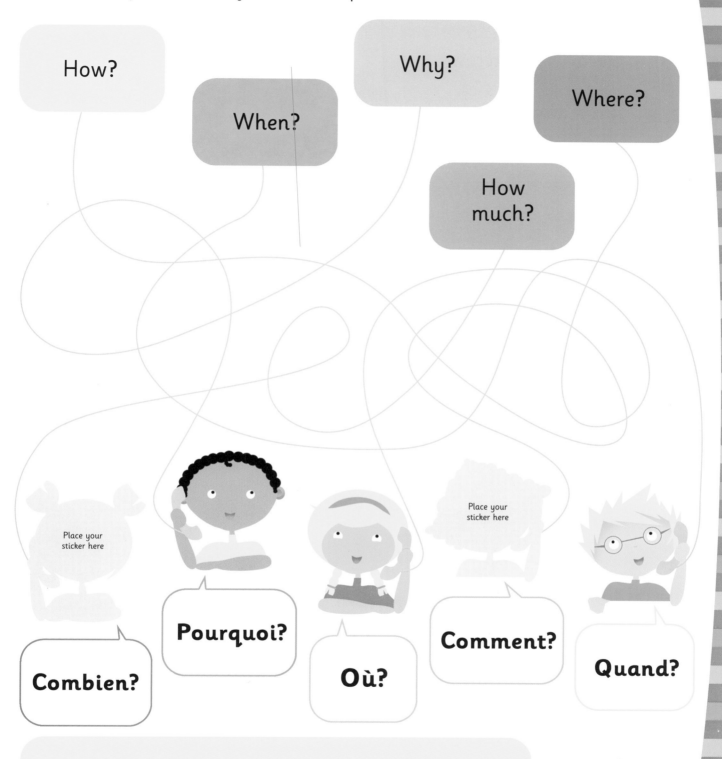

How?

When?

Why?

Where?

How much?

Place your sticker here

Place your sticker here

Place your sticker here

Pourquoi?

Comment?

Combien?

Où?

Quand?

You say it like this:

Comment? (kom-ohn)

Combien? (kom-biyahn)

Quand? (kohn)

Où? (ooh)

Pourquoi? (pour-kwa)

Place your star sticker here

Numbers - nombres

Learn these numbers:

0	**zéro**	(zerow)		7	**sept**	(set)
1	**un / une**	(uhn / oone)		8	**huit**	(wheat)
2	**deux**	(der)		9	**neuf**	(nuf)
3	**trois**	(trwa)		10	**dix**	(dees)
4	**quatre**	(katr)		11	**onze**	(ohns)
5	**cinq**	(sahnk)		12	**douze**	(dooz)
6	**six**	(sees)				

Do the calculations.
Then draw lines to the answers in French.

3 + 1		**huit**
9 – 2		**cinq**
4 + 4		**quatre**
8 + 1		**sept**
7 – 2		**neuf**

Find the sticker and put it in place. Learn these numbers and plural nouns.

un chien – a dog
deux chiens – two dogs

une maison – a house
trois maisons – three houses

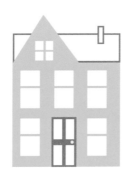

un chat – a cat
quatre chats – four cats

Place your sticker here

Say in French:

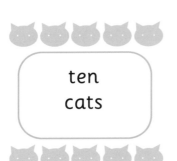

ten cats

six dogs

five houses

Place your star sticker here

Colours - couleurs

Learn these useful colours:

orange
(orahnge)
orange

rose
(rohse)
pink

marron
(marron)
brown

rouge
(rouge)
red

jaune
(johwn)
yellow

The colours below can be either masculine or feminine
to match the nouns they describe.
The 'e' ending matches feminine nouns.

vert / verte	(vair / vairte)	– green
bleu / bleue	(bluh / bluh)	– blue
gris / grise	(gree / greez)	– grey
noir / noire	(noahr / noahr)	– black
blanc / blanche	(blohn / blohnsh)	– white
violet / violette	(vee-olay / vee-olet)	– purple

Place your
star sticker
here

Draw lines to translate these phrases from English to French:

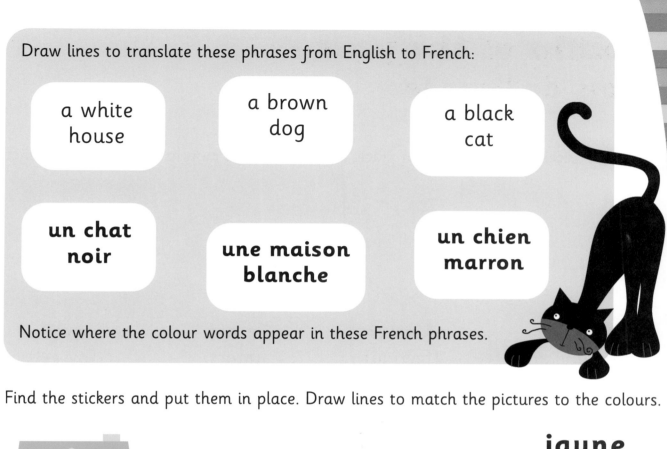

a white house

a brown dog

a black cat

un chat noir

une maison blanche

un chien marron

Notice where the colour words appear in these French phrases.

Find the stickers and put them in place. Draw lines to match the pictures to the colours.

une maison

un chien

jaune

vert

rouge

Place your sticker here

un chat

un tee-shirt

blanc

rose

un arbre

Place your sticker here

une banane

gris

Place your star sticker here

Months of the year - mois de l'année

Find the stickers and put them in place. Learn to say the months of the year in French.

janvier
(jahnviay)
January

février
(fevriay)
February

mars
(mars)
March

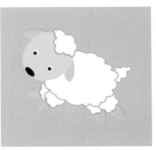

avril
(avreel)
April

mai
(meh)
May

juin
(jwan)
June

juillet
(jweeyay)
July

août
(ooht)
August

septembre
(septahmbr)
September

octobre
(octohbr)
October

novembre
(novahmbr)
November

décembre
(daysahmbr)
December

In French, months and days do not start with a capital letter unless they are at the beginning of a sentence. Say in French:

The month you were born.

The month we are in now.

The month you go on holiday.

Find the days of the week in this wordsearch.

lundi	(lundi)	– Monday
mardi	(mardi)	– Tuesday
mercredi	(mehrcredi)	– Wednesday
jeudi	(jehdi)	– Thursday
vendredi	(vahndredi)	– Friday
samedi	(samdi)	– Saturday
dimanche	(deemahnsh)	– Sunday

v	r	q	r	d	c	x	m	p	b
l	u	n	d	i	i	c	e	v	c
u	a	a	t	m	i	v	r	e	m
b	t	p	y	a	p	b	c	n	k
b	b	w	u	n	m	a	r	d	i
c	x	w	u	c	r	y	e	r	w
d	z	f	h	h	q	q	d	e	d
d	p	r	j	e	u	d	i	d	d
o	s	a	m	e	d	i	k	i	t
w	q	u	z	v	n	p	r	s	u

Place your star sticker here

The time - les heures

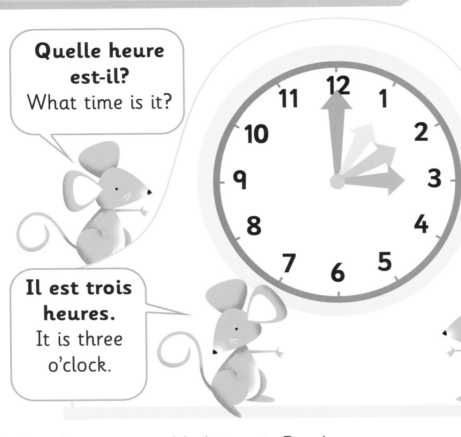

Quelle heure est-il?
What time is it?

Il est une heure.
It is one o'clock.

Il est deux heures.
It is two o'clock.

Il est trois heures.
It is three o'clock.

Write the remaining o'clock times in French.

1. It is four o'clock. _____

2. It is five o'clock. _____

3. It is six o'clock. _____

4. It is seven o'clock. _____

5. It is eight o'clock. _____

6. It is nine o'clock. _____

7. It is ten o'clock. _____

8. It is eleven o'clock. _____

9. It is twelve o'clock. _____

Midi
is midday.

Minuit
is midnight.

Place your star sticker here

Find the sticker and put it in place. Join the times to the clocks.

Place your sticker here

Il est une heure.

Il est six heures.

Il est neuf heures.

Il est onze heures.

Say in French:

et demie
half-past

**deux heures
et demie**
half-past two

Write in French:

It is half-past five. **Il est** _____

It is half-past eight. **Il est** _____

You say it like this:

Quelle heure est-il?   (kell ur et-eel)
midi   (meedi)
minuit   (minwee)

Place your
star sticker
here

Family - la famille

Learn these French words for members of the family.

la mère	(mair)	– mother
le père	(pear)	– father
la fille	(fee)	– daughter
le fils	(fees)	– son
la sœur	(sur)	– sister
le frère	(frair)	– brother
la grand-mère	(grohn-mair)	– grandmother
le grand-père	(grohn-pear)	– grandfather

Place your star sticker here

Find the sticker and put it in place.
Label each person in Clara's family below.

Place your sticker here

Clara

Place your star sticker here

My family - ma famille

Write about yourself and your family. Write the missing words and learn to say these phrases in French. Or you could write about this family, pretending you are Marine.

Sarah

Pascal

Max

Marine

Je m'appelle

My name is

_____

_____

Ma mère s'appelle

My mum is called

_____

_____

Mon père s'appelle

My dad is called

_____

_____

Mon frère s'appelle

My brother is called

_____

_____

Ma soeur s'appelle

My sister is called

_____

_____

Place your
star sticker
here

How many brothers and sisters do you have? Or are you an only child?
Write the missing words to complete these sentences.

J'ai _____ **frère.**

I have _____ brother.

J'ai _____ **soeur.**

I have _____ sister.

J'ai _____ **frères.**

I have _____ brothers.

J'ai _____ **soeurs.**

I have _____ sisters.

Je suis fils/fille unique.

Je suis _____ **unique.**

I'm an only (m/f) child.

Try to read this conversation in French:

Ils s'appellent Evie et Alex.
They are called Evie and Alex.

J'ai une soeur et un frère.
I have a sister and a brother.

Place your star sticker here

Sports - les sports

Let's talk about sport! Follow the conversations in French.

Tu es sportif/sportive?
Are you sporty?

Oui, je suis sportif. (m)
Yes, I am sporty.

Non, je ne suis pas sportive. (f)
No, I am not sporty.

Aimez-vous...?
Do you like...?

J'aime...
I like...

Je n'aime pas...
I don't like...

Say in French:

I like football.

Place your sticker here

I don't like horse riding.

I like ice skating.

Key vocabulary

Le football – football
Le cricket – cricket
La gymnastique – gymnastics
Le ski – skiing
La natation – swimming
L'équitation – horse riding
Le patinage sur glace — ice skating
Le vélo – cycling

You say **sportif** for a boy and **sportive** for a girl.

Place your star sticker here

You say it like this:

sportif/sportive	(sporteef/sporteev)
j'aime	(zhem)
football	(fewtbohl)
cricket	(kreekeht)

gymnastique	(jeemnasteek)
ski	(skee)
natation	(natasyon)
équitation	(ekitasyon)
patinage sur glace	(patinazh suh glass)
vélo	(vaylo)

Follow the lines to find out what these children like to do.

J'aime...

le tennis.
(taynees)

J'aime...

la danse.
(dauns)

J'aime...

la pêche.
(pesch)

dancing

fishing

tennis

Place your
star sticker
here

Animals - les animaux

Avez-vous un animal domestique?
Do you have a pet?

Find the sticker and put it in place.
Try to read the conversation in French:

> **J'ai un chien et un chat.**
> I have a dog and a cat.

> **J'ai un chien.**
> I have a dog.

Place your sticker here

Louis a un chien.
Louis has a dog.

Camille a un chien et un chat.
Camille has a dog and a cat.

Key vocabulary

un chien – dog
un chat – cat
un poisson rouge – goldfish

un oiseau – bird
un lapin – rabbit
un cheval – horse

Place your star sticker here

You say it like this:

quel	(kell)	**oiseau**	(wazo)
préféré	(pray-fair-ay)	**lapin**	(lapahn)
poisson	(pwasohn)	**cheval**	(sheval)

Draw lines to join the French to the English translation.

J'aime les chiens.

I like horses.

J'aime les chiens et les chats.

I like dogs.

J'aime les chevaux.

I like dogs and cats.

Quel est votre animal préféré?
Which is your favourite animal?

Find out its name in French!

Place your star sticker here

The market - le marché

Find the stickers and put them in place. Read the shopping list below.
Find these 10 items from the shopping list in the wordsearch opposite.

Place your sticker here

baguette
stick of bread

oeufs
eggs

fromage
cheese

lait
milk

tomates
tomatoes

gâteau
cake

Place your sticker here

petits pois
peas

bananes
bananas

You say it like this:

baguette	(bagget)
lait	(lay)
oeufs	(euh)
fromage	(fromahjh)
gâteau	(gat-o)
tomates	(tom-at)
petits pois	(petee-pwa)
bananes	(banane)
raisins	(rai-zahn)
pommes	(pom)

raisins
grapes

pommes
apples

Place your star sticker here

Find the French words from the shopping list by looking across and down the wordsearch grid. Circle each word as you find it.

p	o	d	g	m	y	p	p	q	z	m
p	e	t	i	t	p	o	i	s	y	w
c	u	r	f	r	o	m	a	g	e	b
x	f	h	f	w	h	m	m	l	b	a
z	s	t	q	v	r	e	n	p	b	g
b	a	n	a	n	e	s	o	m	p	u
r	g	l	g	q	w	w	m	q	l	e
t	b	a	r	a	i	s	i	n	s	t
u	v	i	e	t	a	p	q	l	w	t
a	c	t	v	g	â	t	e	a	u	e
t	o	m	a	t	e	s	p	p	h	v

Follow this conversation. Translate the reply from French into English.

Vous désirez?
What would you like?

Je voudrais...
I'd like...

Je voudrais deux baguettes et six pommes, s'il vous plaît.

_____

_____

Place your star sticker here

The café - le café

Find the sticker and put it in place.
Read the menus. Repeat the words in French.

La carte
Menu

une soupe
(soop)
soup

un sandwich
(sandweech)
a sandwich

au fromage
(o fromahjh)
with cheese

au jambon
(o jombohn)
with ham

une salade
(sal-ad)
salad

les pommes frites
(pom freet)
chips

un hot dog
(hot dog)
hot dog

Place your sticker here

une crêpe
(crepe)
crêpe

une glace à la fraise
(glass a la frez)
strawberry ice cream

Vous désirez?
What would you like?

Place your star sticker here

Find the sticker and put it in place.

Boissons
Drinks

un jus d'orange
(joo d'orohnj)
orange juice

un thé
(tay)
tea

l'eau minérale
(lo min-ey-ral)
mineral water

un café
(kafay)
coffee

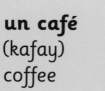

une limonade
(leemon-ad)
lemonade

Place your sticker here

Say in French:

I'd like a strawberry ice cream, please.

I'd like a cheese sandwich and an orange juice, please.

L'addition, s'il vous plaît.
(lad-i-see-ohn, seel voo pleh)
The bill, please.

Place your star sticker here

Clothes - les vêtements

une casquette
(cas-ket)

un tee-shirt
(tee shert)

un jean
(jeen)

les baskets
(bas-ket)

les lunettes de soleil
(loonet duh solay)

un chemisier
(shem-eez-e-ay)

une jupe
(joop)

les chaussures
(show-sur)

Place your
star sticker
here

Draw a picture of yourself here. Label what you are wearing in French.

_____

_____

_____

_____

_____

_____

_____

_____

_____

_____

_____

_____

Find the sticker and put it in place. Look at the pictures below.
Match the colour words to the clothes.

un pantalon
(panta-lohn)

une chemise
(shumees)

une robe
(rohbe)

blanche

gris

marron

vertes

rouge

les bottes
(bott)

Place your
sticker here

les chaussettes
(showset)

Place your
star sticker
here

My home - ma maison

Find the stickers and put them in place.
Learn the key vocabulary opposite.
Complete the missing labels for this house.

la commode

la salle à manger

le salon

la télévision

le sofa

Place your sticker here

Place your sticker here

Place your star sticker here

Key vocabulary

le salon	(salohn)	– living room
la salle à manger	(sal a mahn-jay)	– dining room
la cuisine	(qwizeen)	– kitchen
la salle de bain	(sal duh bahn)	– bathroom
la chambre	(shambr)	– bedroom
la douche	(doosh)	– shower
la télévision	(telay-vis-iyon)	– television
le lit	(lee)	– bed
la armoire	(amwaure)	– wardrobe
la commode	(komode)	– chest of drawers
la chaise	(shez)	– chair
le sofa	(so-fa)	– sofa
la table	(tabl)	– table

Complete the crossword by writing
the French words in the grid.
For the crossword, you can omit
la or **le** before the noun.

Across

1. sofa
2. kitchen
3. wardrobe

Down

1. bed
2. bedroom
3. shower

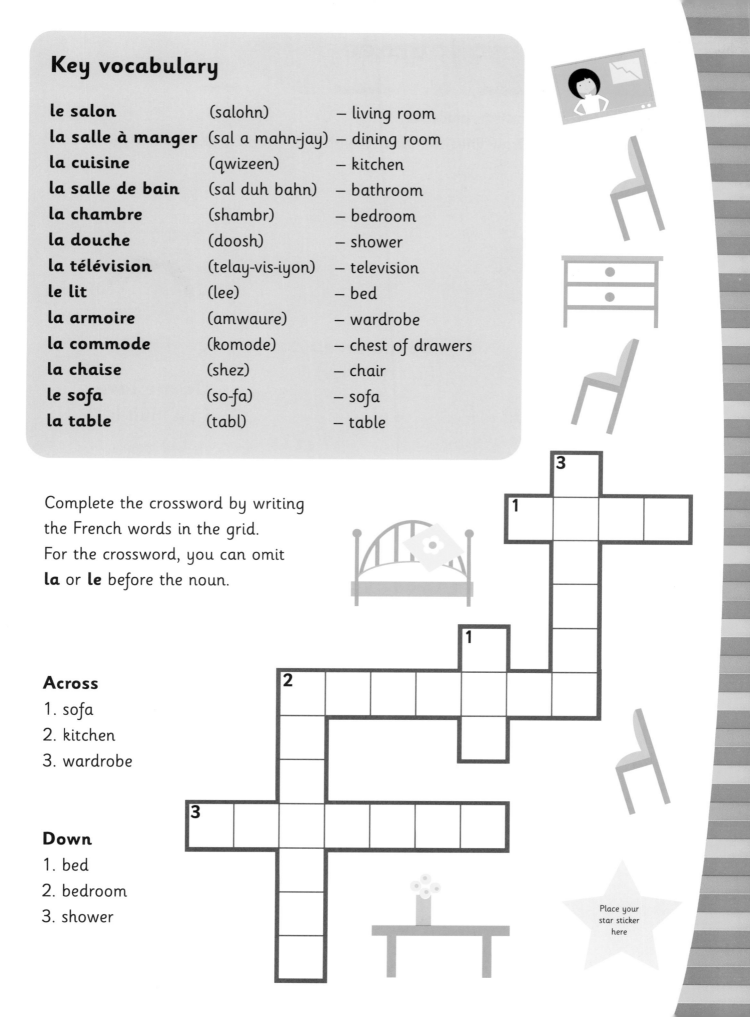

Place your
star sticker
here

My day - ma journée

Find the sticker and put it in place.
Look at the pictures. Draw lines to match the English words to the French words.

Je me réveille.
(juh muh ray-vay-yay)

Place your sticker here

Je me lève.
(juh muh lev)

Je me lave.
(juh muh lav)

I leave the house.

I wash.

I get dressed.

I wake up.

I get up.

I eat breakfast.

Je m'habille.
(juh mah-bee)

Je mange le petit déjeuner.
(juh maunj luh peti day-jun-eh)

Je quitte la maison.
(juh keet la mayzon)

Place your star sticker here

What are these children doing? Follow the lines to find out.

Je regarde la télévision.
(juh regard la telay-vis-iyon)

Je lis un livre.
(juh lee un leevr)

Je joue avec mes amis.
(juh joo avek mez amee)

I read a book.

I play with my friends.

I watch television.

Place your star sticker here

Answers

Let's talk

Thank you very much – **Merci beaucoup.**
What's your name? – **Comment vous appelez-vous?**
I don't understand – **Je ne comprends pas.**
How are you? – **Ça va?**
How?   **Comment?**
How much?   **Combien?**
When?   **Quand?**
Where?   **Où?**
Why?   **Pourquoi?**

Numbers

3 + 1 = **quatre**   8 + 1 = **neuf**
9 – 2 = **sept**   7 – 2 = **cinq**
4 + 4 = **huit**
ten cats – **dix chats**
six dogs – **six chiens**
five houses – **cinq maisons**

Colours

a white house – **une maison blanche**
a brown dog – **un chien marron**
a black cat – **un chat noir**

une maison rose   **un tee-shirt rouge**
un chien blanc   **un arbre vert**
un chat gris   **une banane jaune**

Days of the week

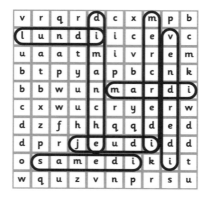

The time

1. **Il est quatre heures.**
2. **Il est cinq heures.**
3. **Il est six heures.**
4. **Il est sept heures.**
5. **Il est huit heures.**
6. **Il est neuf heures.**
7. **Il est dix heures.**
8. **Il est onze heures.**
9. **Il est douze heures.**

Il est six heures.   Il est une heure.

Il est onze heures.   Il est neuf heures.

Il est cinq heures et demie – It is half-past five.
Il est huit heures et demie – It is half-past eight.

Family

le père
father

le grand-père
grandfather

la mère
mother

la grand-mère
grandmother

la soeur
sister

le frère
brother

My family One possible answer:
Je m'appelle Marine.   **Ma mère s'appelle Sarah.**
Mon père s'appelle Pascal. Mon frère s'appelle Max.

Sports

J'aime le football – I like football.
Je n'aime pas l'équitation – I don't like horse riding.
J'aime le patinage sur glace – I like ice skating.
J'aime le tennis – tennis.
J'aime la danse – dancing.
J'aime la pêche – fishing.

Animals

J'aime les chiens – I like dogs.
J'aime les chiens et les chats – I like dogs and cats.
J'aime les chevaux – I like horses.

The market

**Je voudrais
deux baguettes
et six pommes,
s'il vous plaît.**
I'd like two sticks
of bread and
six apples, please.

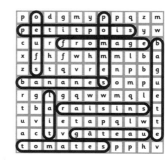

The café

I'd like a strawberry ice cream, please.
Je voudrais une glace à la fraise, s'il vous plaît.
I'd like a cheese sandwich and an orange juice, please.
**Je voudrais un sandwich au fromage et un jus
d'orange, s'il vous plaît.**

Clothes

un pantalon gris
grey trousers
une chemise blanche
white shirt
une robe rouge
red dress
les bottes marron
brown boots
les chaussettes vertes
green socks

My home

My day

Je me réveille – I wake up.   **Je me lève** – I get up.
Je me lave – I wash.   **Je m'habille** – I get dressed.
Je mange le petit déjeuner – I eat breakfast.
Je quitte la maison – I leave the house.
Je joue avec mes amis – I play with my friends.
Je regarde la télévision – I watch television.
Je lis un livre – I read a book.